Look for the Robin

Written by Jane Somers

Illustrated by Jeannie Duncanson

In memory of Mum and Dad.

Mum once said to me

"Know that you are loved"

And I still do.

For my sons; James, Liam, Joe and Niall.

"Know that you are loved."

Copyright 2023 J M Somers

'Look for the Robin'

Acknowledgements

For my family and friends who have always encouraged me to write. Now, after so many years, I'm finally listening!

Thank you to Michael Heppell and everyone involved in his Write That Book challenge, which gave me the impetus to get my book over the line.

Thanks to two lovely ladies: Jeannie Duncanson for your amazing illustrations and guidance and Diane Hull, my patient editor.

. . . .

I hope my book brings comfort

to any child who is missing

someone special.

This book is in memory of

....

....

Look for the Robin

Let's begin...

Here's a lovely story;
I wonder if you've heard,
About a friendly robin,
a very clever bird.

Anyone who's lost someone
needs to take a look,
At robin's special message
found inside this book.

Look out of your
window;

Find the brightest
star.

You have found your loved one;
that is where they are.

Though they may be far away,
far away from sight,
Their love will keep on shining,
lighting up the night.

When your special loved one

wants a closer view,

They will ask a robin

to come and visit you.

A special bird they've chosen,

is sent from high above.

Their chest bright red and beautiful,

glowing with their love.

Your loved one may be gone now,
but they will find a way,
To come and say hello
and brighten up your day.

That's why friendly robins
will fly that extra mile,
Just to land beside you
to try and make you smile.

Sometimes little robins can be rather shy.
They may hide and watch you from a
place nearby.

Waiting there and hoping
to catch a smile from you.
Then they'll tell your loved one
and they'll be smiling too.

If your loved one sends you a pretty,
pure white feather,

It shows you that your hearts are
intertwined forever.

Those feathers are a sign,
a truly magic touch,

To show you they are still around and
you are loved so much.

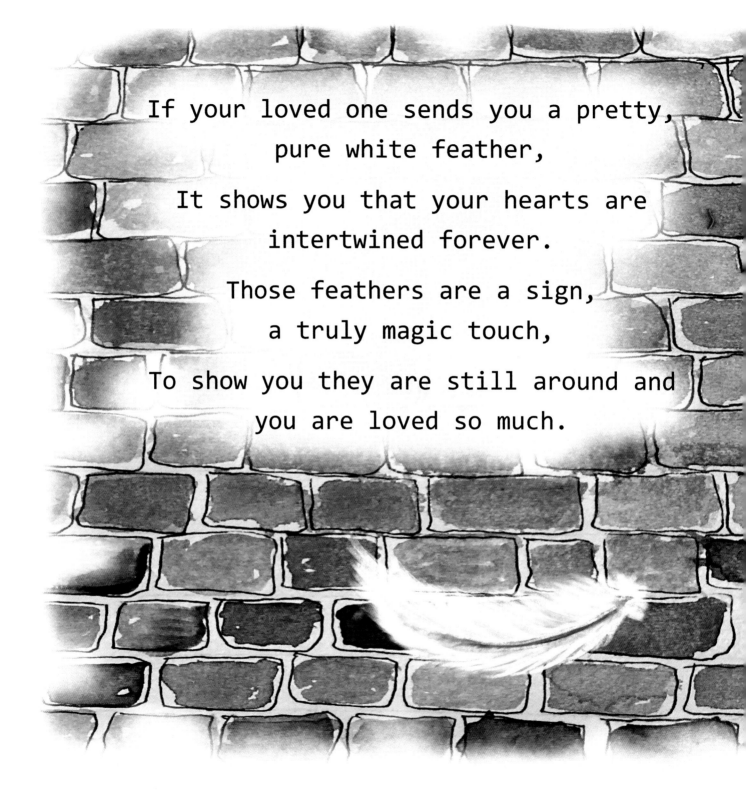

Losing someone close to you
can make you feel so sad.
Treasure all the happy times
and let your heart feel glad.

Then, if little robin

comes visiting one day,

Share your special message;

something you might say.

Then that lovely robin will
take off through the skies.

Your whispered message on their
wings, upward robin flies.

Holding all your kisses
and carrying your love.
Heading to your loved one,
waiting up above.

So, when you see a robin,
it means someone wants to say,
"I look down and I love you,
every night and day.

Though you cannot see me,
you know I've not gone far.
Just look out for the robin,
that feather or bright star."

The End

My message to Mum and Dad
(The inspiration behind this book)

There are still some sad days when I shed a tear.
But, when I see the robin, I know that you are near.

Thanks for watching over me from high up above
And for finding ways to make me feel your love.

I want you to know I'm still thinking of you too.
You're always in my heart and in everything I do.

To order more or ask Jane any questions, please contact her at:-

Email: askjane@janesomersauthor.com